PreScripts

CURSIVE WORDS AND DRAWING

Math Terms

CLASSICALCONVERSATIONS.COM

PreScripts Cursive Words and Drawing: Math Terms

Published in the U.S.A. by Classical Conversations, Inc.
P.O. Box 909
West End, NC 27376

ISBN: 978-0-9884965-8-3
For ordering information, visit www.ClassicalConversationsBooks.com.
Printed in the United States of America

PreScripts
Cursive Words and Drawing: Math Terms

A Note for Parents 6

Forming the Cursive Letters 8

Math Terms in Cursive Copywork and Drawing 11

Index of Math Terms Used in Cursive Copywork 145

Index of Terms Used in Drawing Lessons 146

Related Products For Classical Education....................................147

A Note for Parents: Tools for the Journey

Introduction

The word "prescript" comes from the Latin words *prae* (meaning "before," "in front of") + *scribere* ("to write"). The PreScripts series from Classical Conversations MultiMedia is designed to precede—to come before—writing. Just as we learn to speak by mimicking our parents' words, we can learn to write well by copying the words that others have written. Even though coloring, drawing, tracing, and copying are simple tasks from an adult perspective, imitation is at the heart of a classical education. In order to learn how to write, children must first acquire fine motor skills and learn to sit still and follow instructions. They do so with the help of simple tasks like these. Rather than resorting to mindless busywork that isolates young children from their family's education, the PreScripts series is designed to initiate young learners into the world of knowledge they will inhabit as they mature.

Each book in the PreScripts series combines a functional design with excellent content. The goal of *Cursive Words and Drawing* is to establish the building blocks of cursive writing: letters first, then words, and then simple sentences. Your students will practice each letter, first tracing it, and then writing it, keeping the model nearby. As they gain confidence and skill, they will trace and write simple sentences.

Our job as classical educators is to teach students to make the effort to be neat but preferably to aim higher by teaching them to write beautifully. Many schools no longer teach cursive writing, claiming that it is too difficult for young children to master. Teaching a child to write in cursive does require diligence and patience, but it has a number of compelling benefits. Research suggests that cursive writing more effectively develops manual skill and dexterity. Cursive may also aid students struggling with dyslexia or dysgraphia because 1) capital and lowercase letters are distinct; 2) each word is one fluid movement, so the child's rhythm is not disrupted by frequent pauses; and 3) letters like "b" and "d" are more difficult to reverse.

While they master the manual skill of writing, students will also begin to pick up basic writing and reading rules. They will start to notice that every sentence begins with a capital letter and ends with an end mark, that items in a list are separated by commas, that names are capitalized, etc. When your child becomes curious, take a moment to explain these rules. As a result, writing correctly will come more naturally to them when it is time to compose their own sentences.

How to Use This Book

When children are learning to read and write, what they study matters as much as how they study it. Parents are more likely to give up on cursive when the content seems frivolous, so Classical Conversations is pleased to offer cursive writing books that give the student plenty of practice using rich, meaningful content. With PreScripts cursive writing books, your student can become a confident writer while learning or reviewing important subject matter, such as history sentences, passages of literature, and science or math definitions.

Although variety is important, the key to mastering cursive is to practice every day. For best results, set aside a specific time each day for cursive practice. You choose the pace appropriate for your child. You can assign one page a day to a beginning student or assign two to four pages a day to an older or more experienced student. A very young student, or one who struggles with writing, might even do half a page a day until his or her fine motor skills become stronger, working up to a page or two a day. The pace is completely up to the parent.

If you choose to do one page a day, you should have enough pages for a complete school year, completing approximately four or five pages a week. If you participate in a Classical Conversations community, you can do four pages a week while your community meets, and five pages a week the rest of the school year. Older children might do two pages a day and complete two books a year. If you would like your child to memorize the math terms in this book, you can read through the terms weekly to review or have your student do the same book twice.

Math and the Natural World

In this book, we will focus on the definitions of important math terms related to the operations of arithmetic, basic shapes, measurements, and number forms. Math is a language like any other, but very few students learn its vocabulary—what classical educators refer to as the grammar of mathematics. If children are exposed to these core math concepts when they are young, they can focus on understanding the concepts as they mature. *PreScripts Cursive Words and Drawing: Math Terms* gives children a firm foundation in the grammar of mathematics to prepare them for a lifetime of playing with numbers.

The terms in this book are arranged in alphabetical order rather than in the unit studies you might find in a formal math curriculum. Children in the early stages of learning need to encounter all kinds of facts before they are asked to connect the dots between them. Your child will see the same words repeatedly as he completes the book: for example, he might come across the word "parallel" once in a definition, again in a related definition, and a third time a few pages later. Repeating the same information many times in different ways is key to effective memory work.

In addition to the copy work, drawing lessons are sprinkled throughout the book. Drawing provides some variety for your child, but it also helps to develop the fine motor skills necessary for writing and provides practice in sitting still and working independently. The exercises are simple enough for your child to do independently. If you wish to extend the drawing time further, you may want to encourage your child to color his drawings. Even coloring will help your child develop his fine motor skills and improve his stamina for writing in a fun, creative exercise.

This book begins with simple forms and progresses to more complicated step-by-step drawings of mathematical concepts in nature, such as symmetry and patterns. Your child will enjoy learning to draw the radial symmetry of an orange slice and the spirals in a nautilus shell. Spurred by what he has learned, he will delight in searching for other examples in the world around him.

The Journey in Perspective

The key to good writing is daily practice. The key to a heart that seeks truth, beauty, and goodness is providing quality content to copy. We hope you will find both in *PreScripts: Cursive Words and Drawing: Math Terms*.

The goal of the PreScripts series is for your children to master the skills of copying and writing in the context of a biblical worldview, building on a second meaning of the word "prescript." A prescript can also mean a command, rule, or moral guideline. The Bible instructs parents to remember the commandments of God and teach them to their children.

Deuteronomy 6:6–9 reads, "And these words which I command you today shall be in your heart. You shall teach them diligently to your children, and shall talk of them when you sit in your house, when you walk by the way, when you lie down, and when you rise up. You shall bind them as a sign on your hand, and they shall be as frontlets between your eyes. You shall write them on the doorposts of your house and on your gates." As this Scripture reminds us, writing, memorizing, and reciting are all forms of worship that we model for our children.

Let's get started!

Forming the Cursive Letters

Trace, then write each letter.

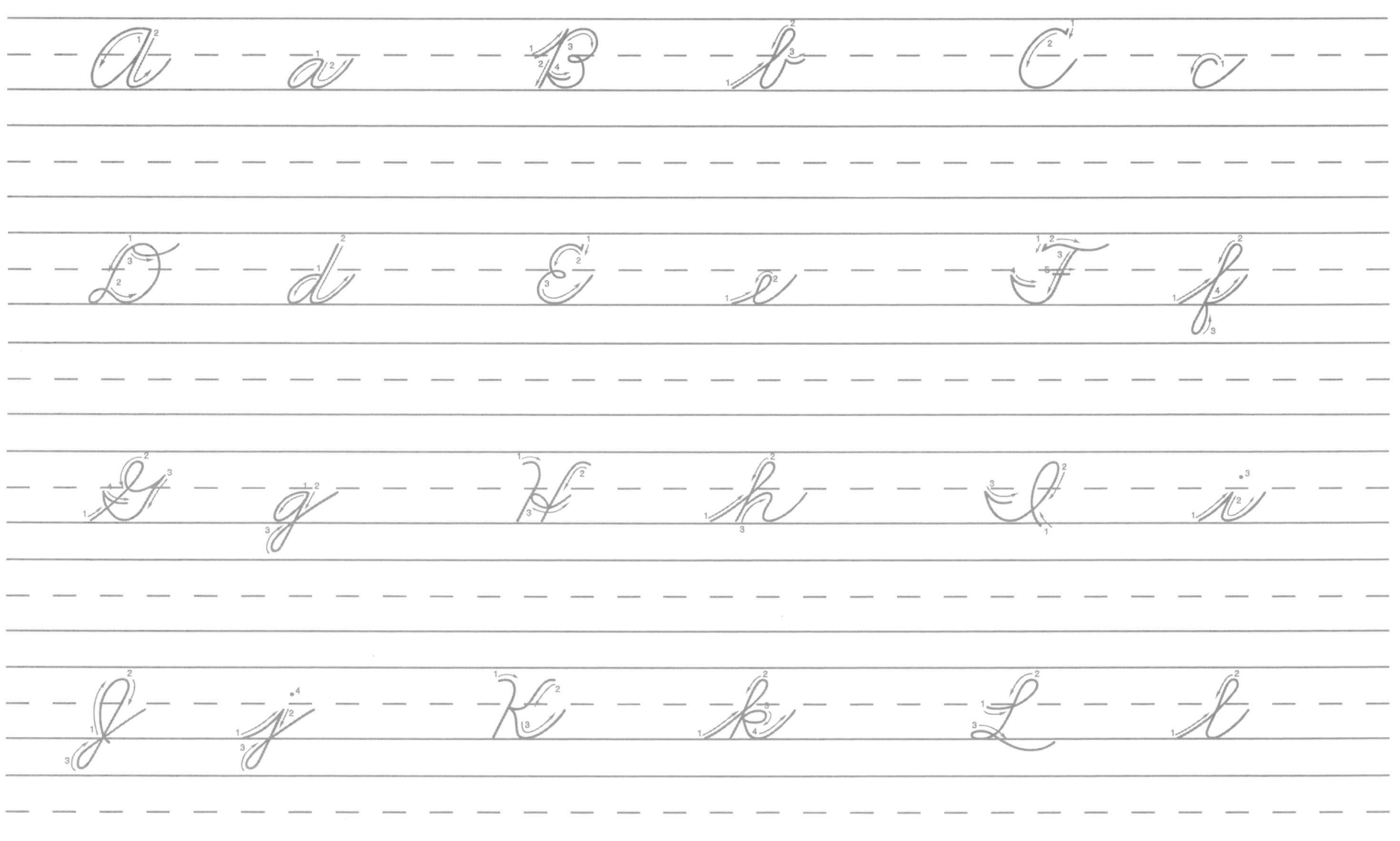

Trace, then write each letter.

Trace, then write each letter.

Write your name in cursive.

$\mathcal{A}$ a

Trace, then write.

$\mathcal{A}$ — — $\mathcal{A}$ — — $\mathcal{A}$ — — $\mathcal{A}$

a — a — a — a — a

Acute — — — — — acute

An acute angle is an angle that

measures less than 90 degrees.

A a

Trace, then write.

A   A   A   A

a   a   a   a   a

Addend   addend

In addition, each of the numbers

brought together is an addend.

Sphere

The shape of a ball or an orange is called a sphere. Shading the lower area and one side can make a circle look like a sphere.

A a

Trace, then write.

Addition   addition

Addition is an operation that brings

two or more numbers together to make

a new total.

Trace, then write.

𝒜𝒶

𝒜 𝒶 𝒜 𝒶

𝒶 𝒶 𝒶 𝒶 𝒶

Angle   angle

An angle is the space created when two

lines diverge from a common point.

Angles are measured in degrees.

Five-pointed Star

On the top of a tomato, there are five leaves that form a star shape. If you draw five straight lines to connect the tips of the leaves, you will form a pentagon, a five-sided shape.

A a

Trace, then write.

a   a   a   a

a   a   a   a   a

Area   area

Area measures the size of a

two-dimensional shape in square units.

A a

Trace, then write.

A   A   A   A

a   a   a   a   a

Associative Law

The associative law of addition states

that the grouping of addends does not

affect their sum.

Cone

A volcano is a cone shape. It is circular at the base and comes up to a point at the top.

$\mathcal{A}$ a

Trace, then write.

$\mathcal{A}$ $\mathcal{A}$ $\mathcal{A}$ $\mathcal{A}$

a a a a a

Associative Law

The associative law of multiplication

states that the grouping of factors does

not affect their product.

Trace, then write.

Bisect   bisect

To bisect is to divide a segment or angle

into two equal parts.

Concentric Circles

Concentric circles are circles that share the same center point. One is inside another. The rings of a tree are concentric circles. The number of rings tells you how old the tree is; each ring equals one year.

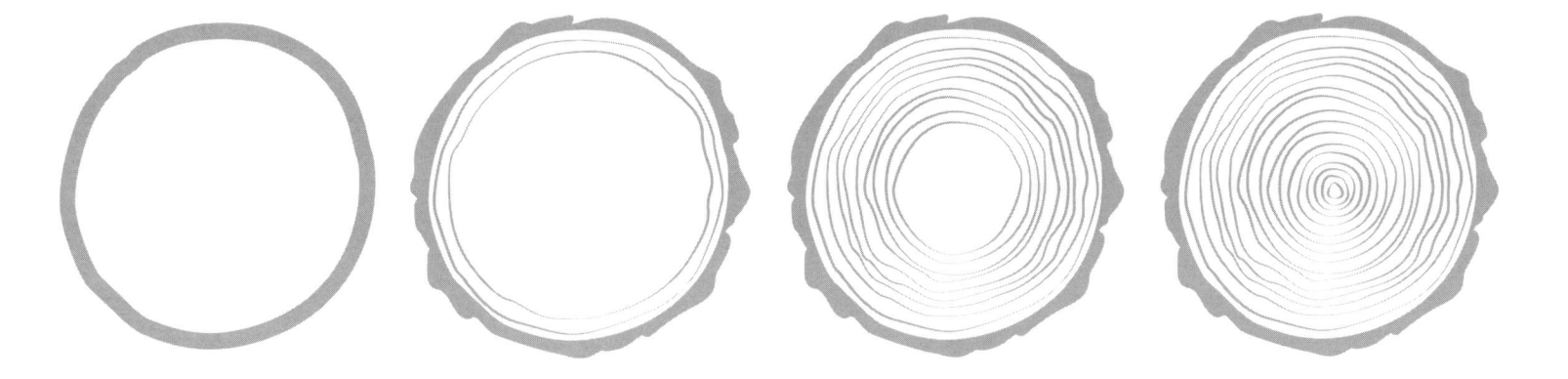

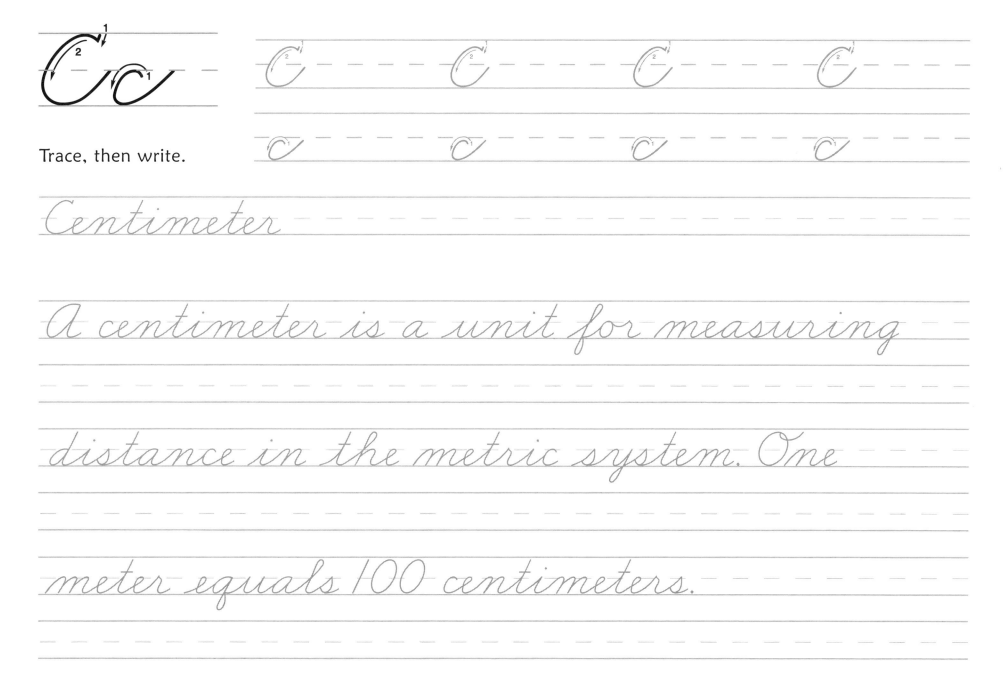

Trace, then write.

Centimeter

A centimeter is a unit for measuring

distance in the metric system. One

meter equals 100 centimeters.

Cc

Trace, then write.

Circle   circle

A circle is a two-dimensional, curved

shape in which all points are the

same distance from the center.

Alternating Patterns

The pattern formed by the veins of this leaf is alternating. Some leaves have veins that are perfectly symmetrical. See if you can find samples of each leaf pattern the next time you go outside.

Cc

Trace, then write.

Circumference

Circumference is the distance around

the outside of a circle.

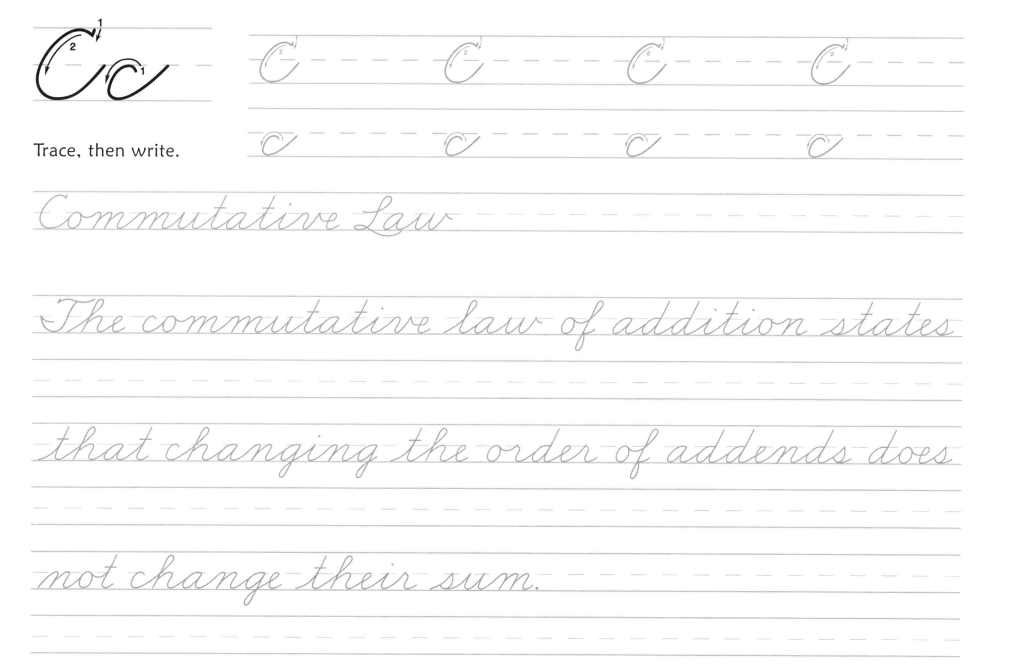

Trace, then write.

Commutative Law

The commutative law of addition states

that changing the order of addends does

not change their sum.

Five-pointed Star

The seeds in an apple are often arranged in a five-pointed star shape.

If you draw lines connecting the outer tips of the seeds, you can form a pentagon, a five-sided shape.

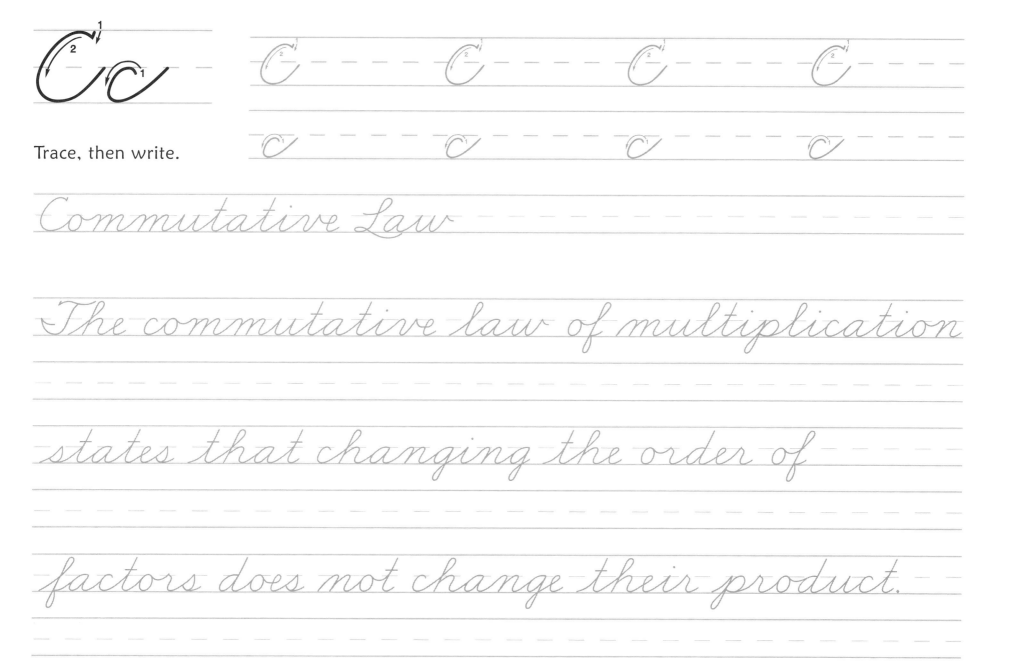

Trace, then write.

Commutative Law

The commutative law of multiplication

states that changing the order of

factors does not change their product.

Trace, then write.

Cone   cone

A cone is a solid shape with one

circular face and a point at the other

end, connected by a curved surface.

Five-pointed Star

The star fruit grows in a five-pointed star shape. The star shape is revealed when the star fruit is sliced in half.

Cc

Trace, then write.

Cube   cube

A cube is a solid shape with six square

faces.

Trace, then write.

Cylinder   cylinder

A cylinder is a solid shape with a

circular face on each end, connected by

a curved surface.

Set of Three

Clover usually grows its leaves in sets of three. The markings on the leaves form a triangle.

Trace, then write.

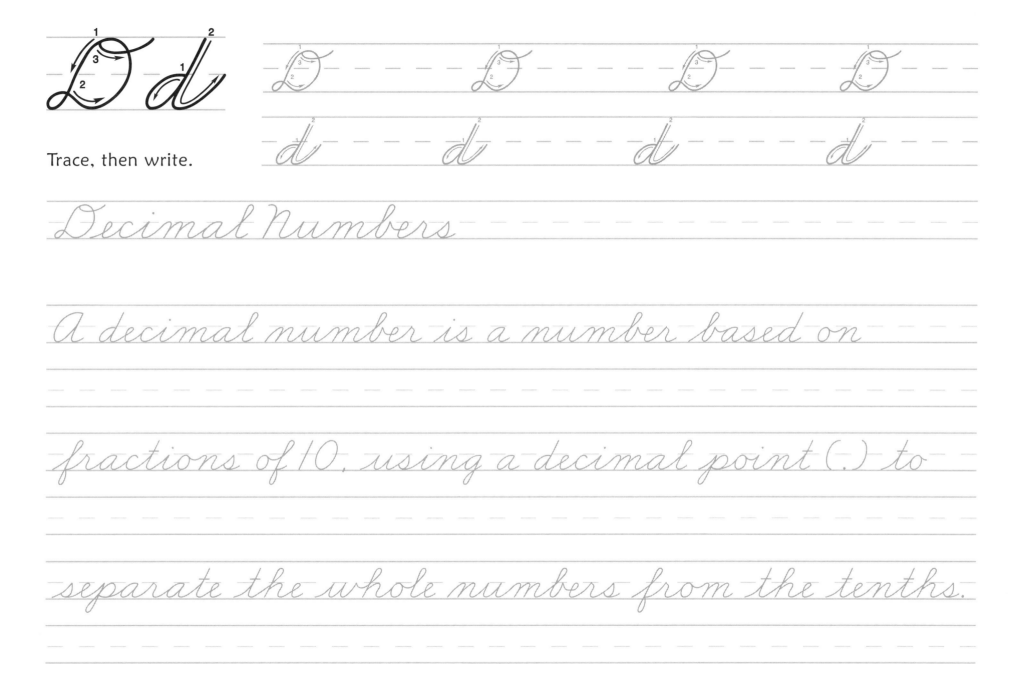

Decimal Numbers

A decimal number is a number based on

fractions of 10, using a decimal point (.) to

separate the whole numbers from the tenths.

Dd

Trace, then write.

Dd   Dd   Dd   Dd

Degree   degree

A degree is a unit for measuring angles.

There are 360 degrees in a circle.

Free Drawing

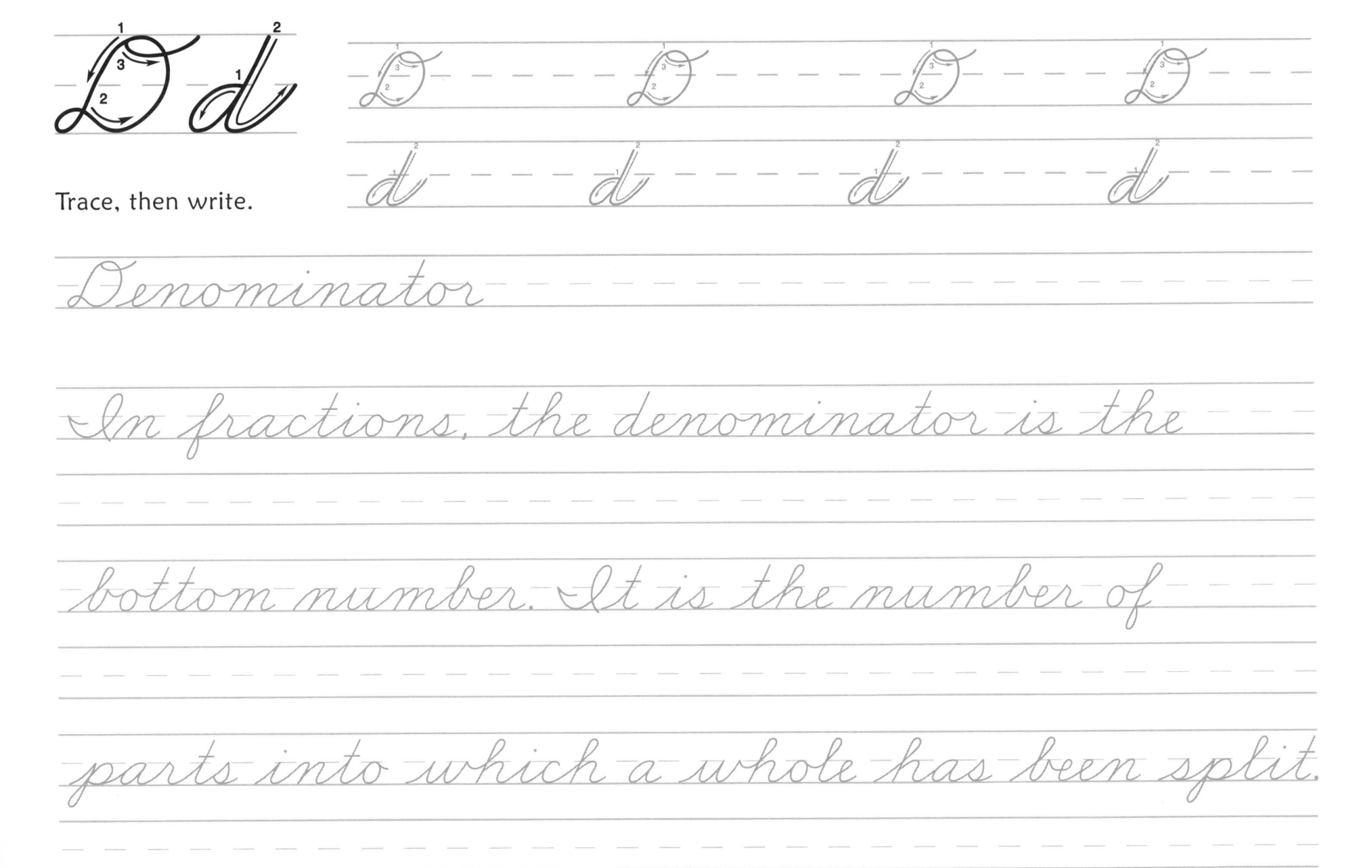

Trace, then write.

Denominator

In fractions, the denominator is the

bottom number. It is the number of

parts into which a whole has been split.

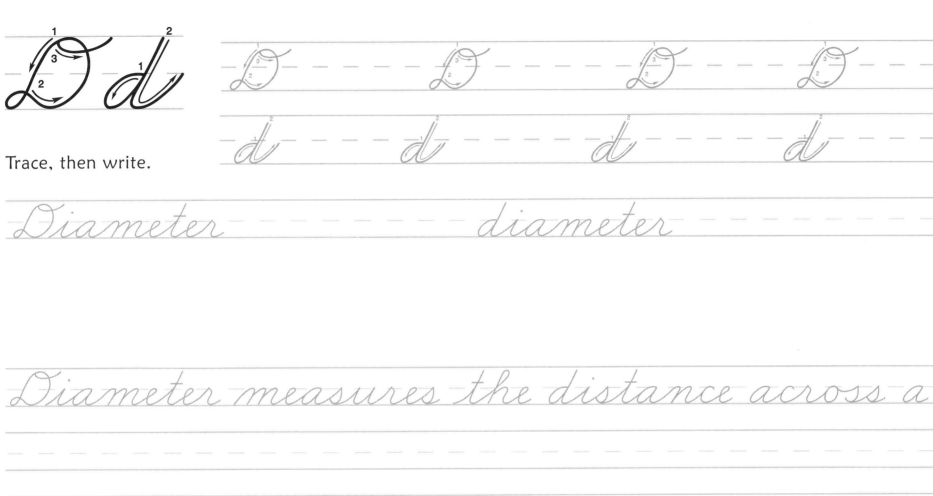

Trace, then write.

Diameter   diameter

Diameter measures the distance across a

circle through its center.

Radial Symmetry

When you slice an orange, you can see lines that radiate out from one point in the center like a wagon wheel. This is called radial symmetry.

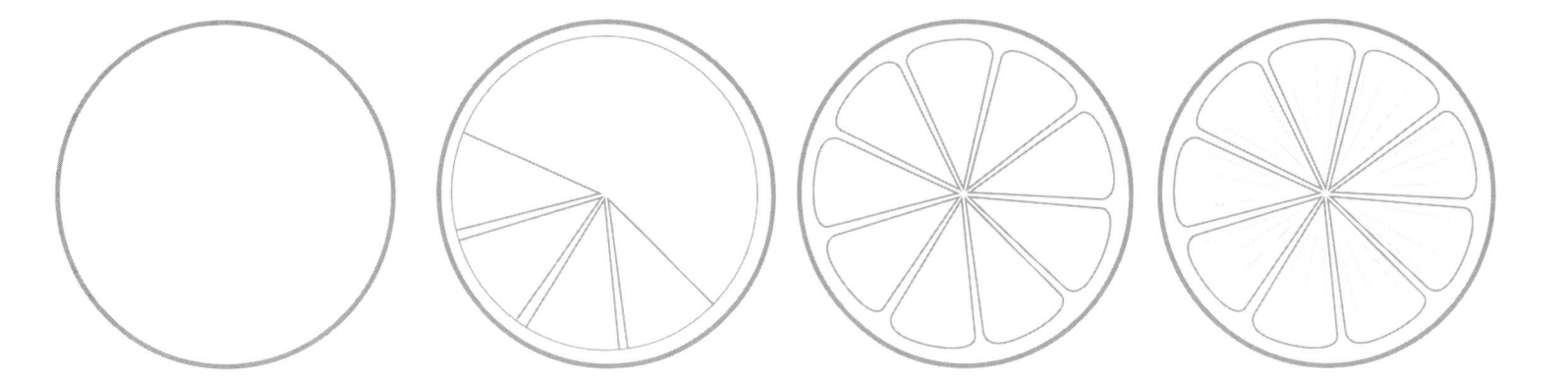

D d

Trace, then write.

Difference   difference

In subtraction, the difference is the

result of taking one number away from

another.

D d

Trace, then write.

Distributive Law

Trace.

The distributive law states that
multiplying a number by a sum yields
the same product as multiplying the
number by each addend and then
adding the products.

Five-pointed Star

This unique animal forms a five-pointed star with its long, skinny legs. It is called a brittle starfish.

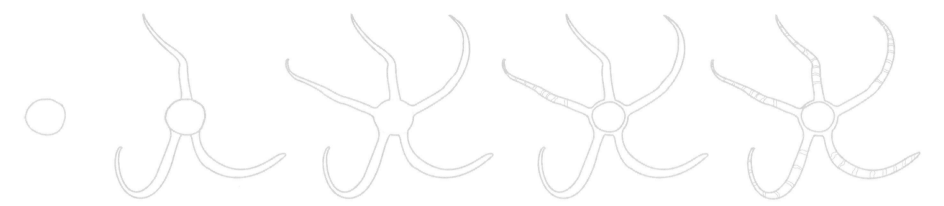

$\mathcal{D}\, d$

Trace, then write.

$\mathcal{D}$ $\mathcal{D}$ $\mathcal{D}$ $\mathcal{D}$

d d d d

Dividend   dividend

In division, the dividend is the

number that is split into a certain

number of parts.

Trace, then write.

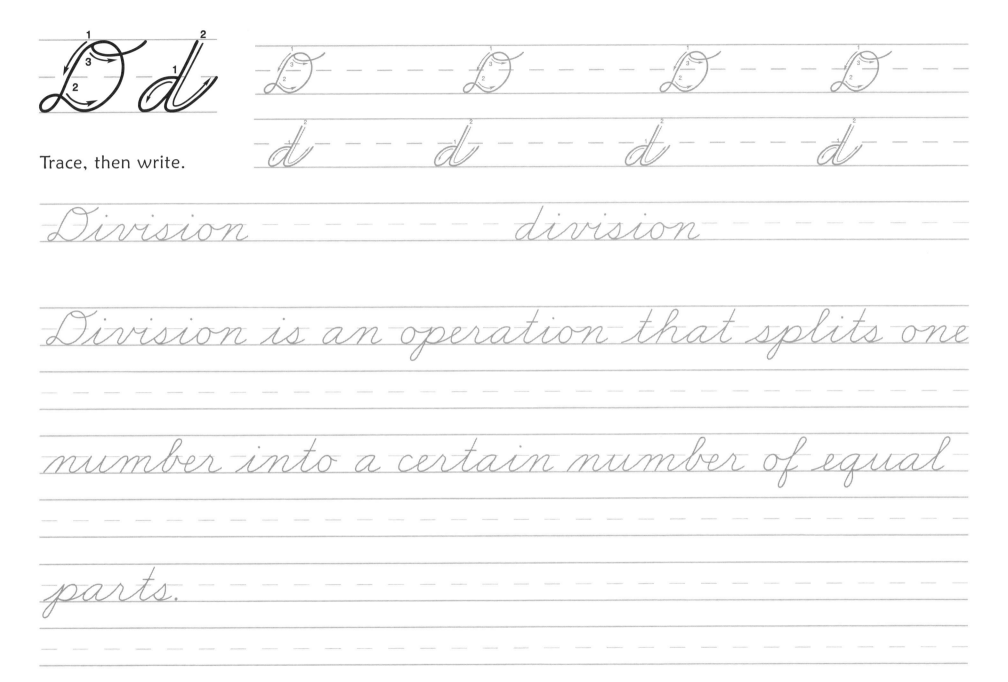

Division   division

Division is an operation that splits one

number into a certain number of equal

parts.

Hexagon

A hexagon is a shape that has six sides that are all the same length.
Bees build perfect hexagons to store their honey.

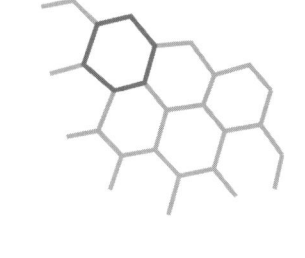 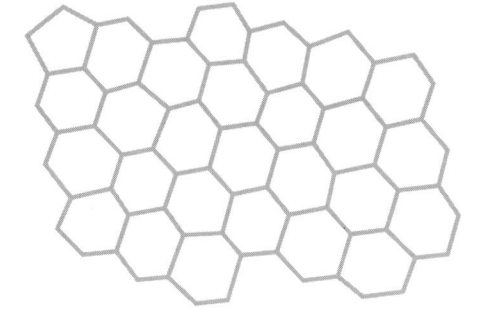 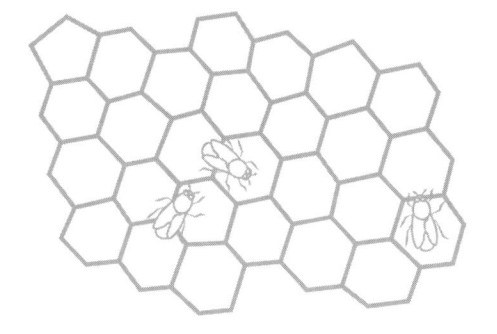

D d

Trace, then write.

Divisor   divisor

In division, the divisor is the

number of parts into which the

dividend is split.

Trace, then write.

Equation   equation

An equation is a statement. It uses " = "

to show that two things are equal.

Set of Four

Usually clover grows three leaves, but sometimes you can find a four-leaf clover.
Notice that the markings on the leaves form a square.

Trace, then write.

Equilateral

An equilateral triangle is a triangle

in which all sides are the same length.

Trace, then write.

Even Numbers

An even number is a number that can

be divided by 2, leaving no remainder.

Symmetry

Symmetry often occurs in nature. Notice how the leaves on this branch are like mirror images of each other; they are symmetrical. If you can draw a line down the center of something and each side is the same, the object is symmetrical. The branch is the line of symmetry for these leaves.

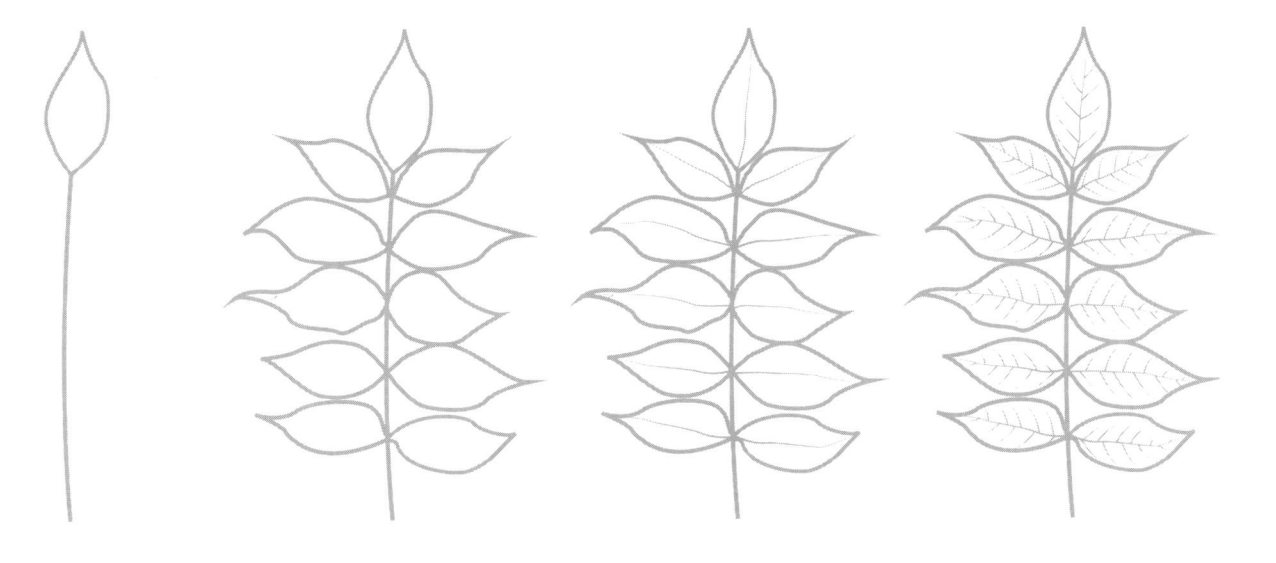

Trace, then write.

F F F F

f f f f

Factor   factor

In multiplication, a factor is a

common name for the number being

added repeatedly.

Trace, then write.

Fibonacci Numbers

Trace.

The Fibonacci numbers are a series of
numbers found by adding the first
two numbers to find the third.
The next number is found by adding
the previous two numbers: 0, 1, 1, 2, 3, 5,
8, 13, etc.

One

The calla lily has only one petal. It is a cone shape.

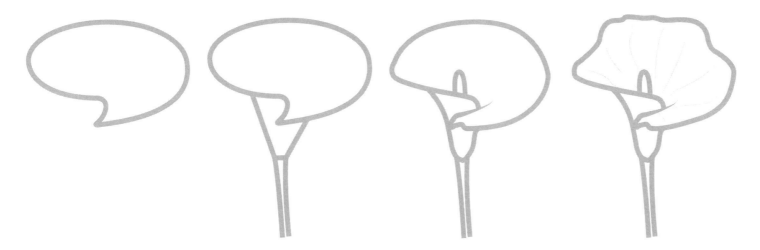

Trace, then write.

Foot   foot

A foot is a unit of measuring distance.

One foot equals twelve inches; three feet

equals one yard.

Trace, then write.

Fraction   fraction

A fraction is a number expressing

parts of a whole.

Set of Three

This tomato slice reveals three-way symmetry. From the center point, three lines radiate out. Each of the three sections is identical.

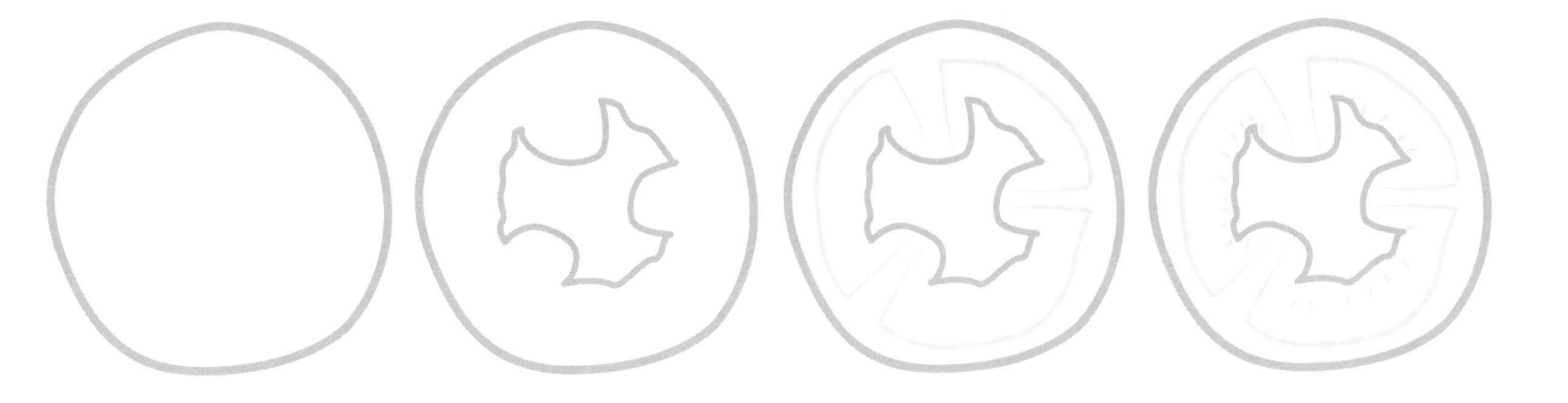

Trace, then write.

Gg

Geometry   geometry

Geometry is a branch of math that

deals with shapes and sizes.

Trace, then write.

Height

Height means the vertical distance

from the top to the bottom of an object.

Set of Three

A trillium flower has three petals. If you draw three lines connecting the three tips of the petals, you can form a triangle, a shape with three sides.

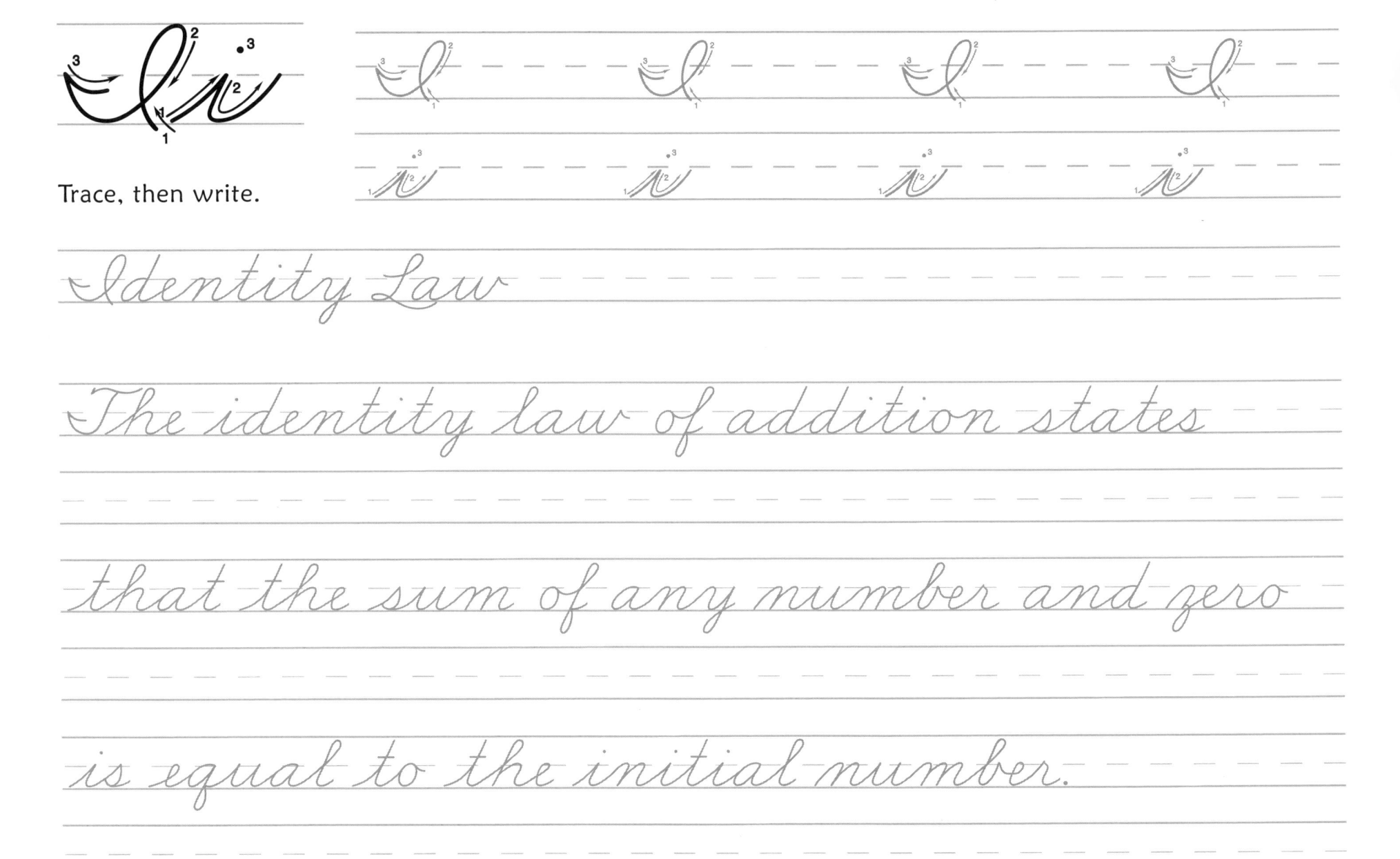

Trace, then write.

Identity Law

The identity law of addition states

that the sum of any number and zero

is equal to the initial number.

Trace, then write.

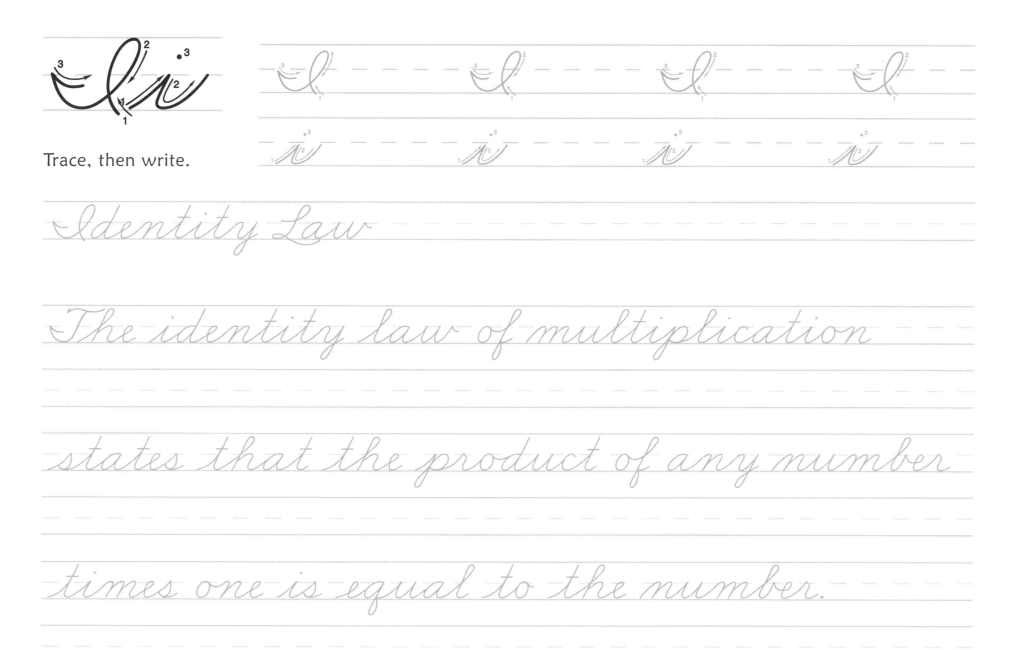

Identity Law

The identity law of multiplication

states that the product of any number

times one is equal to the number.

Free Drawing

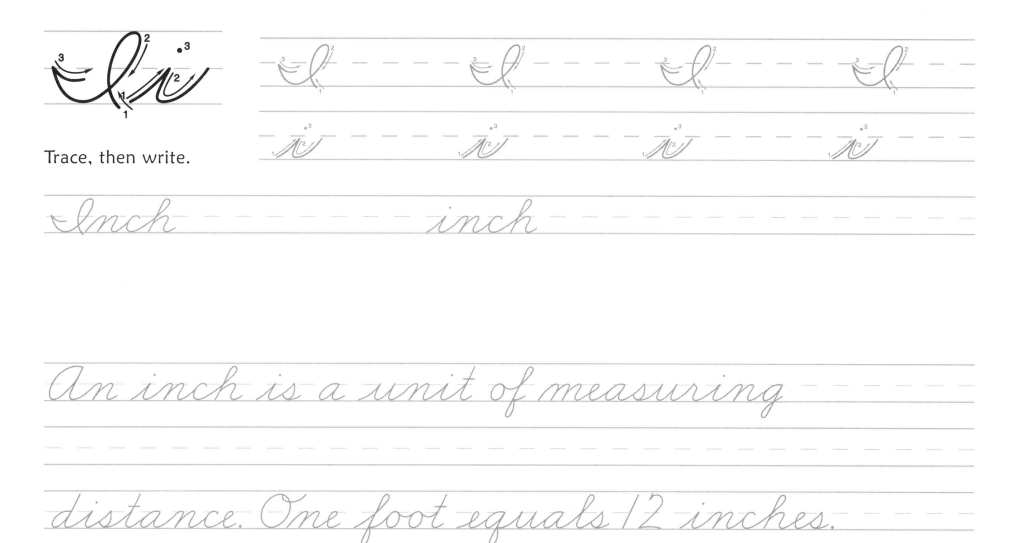

Trace, then write.

Inch   inch

An inch is a unit of measuring

distance. One foot equals 12 inches.

An integer belongs to a set of numbers

(...-3, -2, -1, 0, 1, 2, 3...) that can be

written without a fraction or decimal.

Integers can be positive or negative.

Trace.

Integer   Integer

Trace, then write.

Set of Five

The columbine flower has two sets of five petals. If you draw straight lines to connect the tips of the petals, you can form two pentagons, one inside the other.

Trace, then write.

Intersect   *intersect*

To intersect is to share a common point

or points.

Trace, then write.

Isosceles   isosceles

An isosceles triangle is a triangle with

at least two sides of equal length.

Set of Four

A dogwood tree grows flowers that always have four petals. They form the shape of a cross.

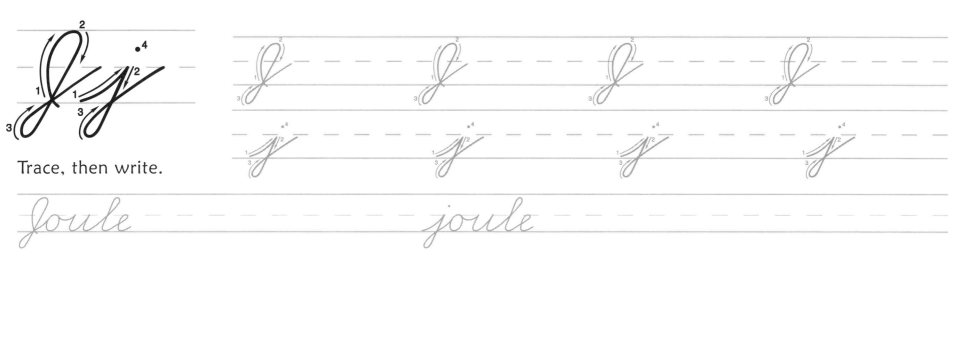

Trace, then write.

Joule   *joule*

A joule is a unit for measuring heat,

work, or energy.

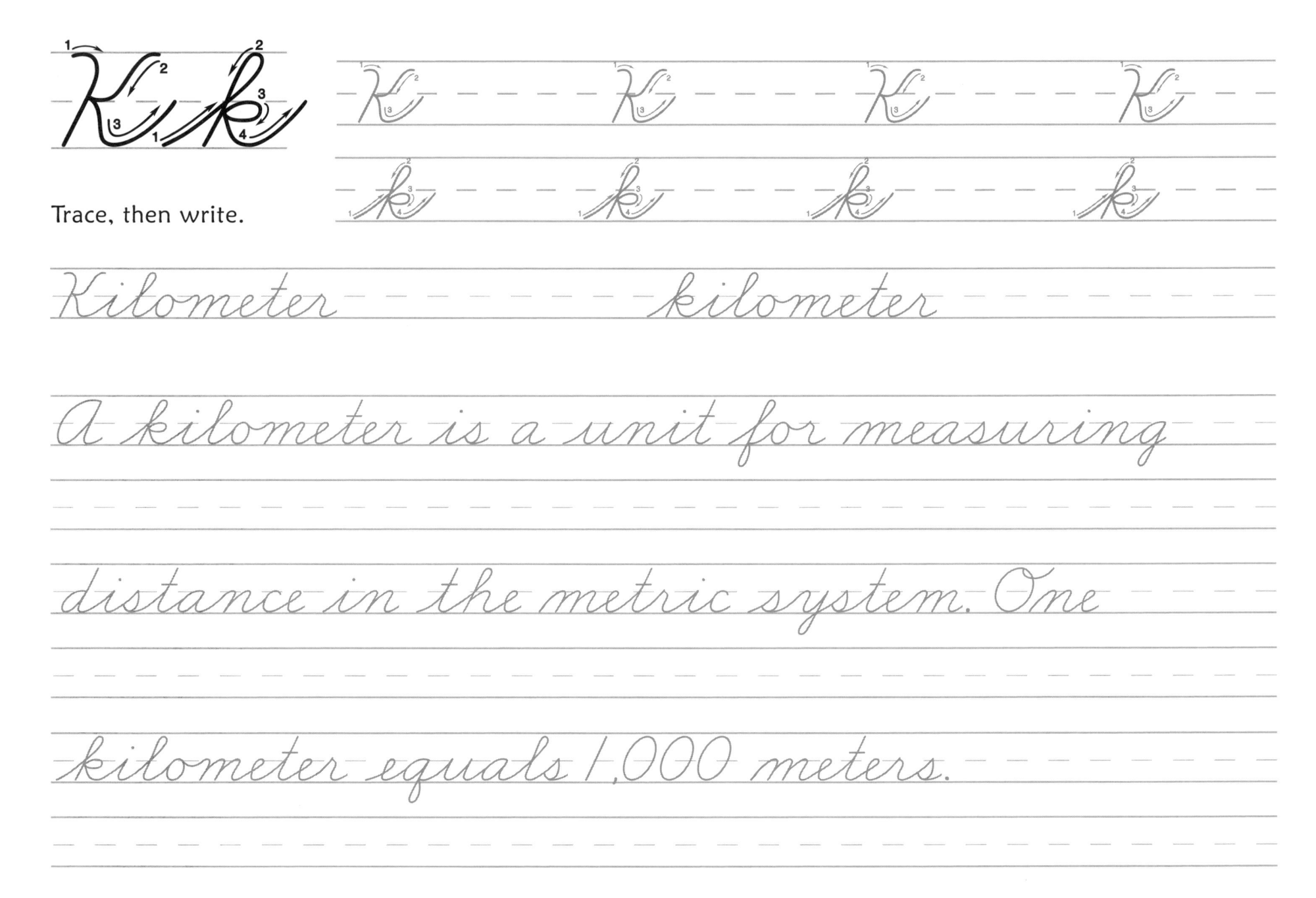

Trace, then write.

Kilometer   kilometer

A kilometer is a unit for measuring

distance in the metric system. One

kilometer equals 1,000 meters.

Radial Symmetry

This spider web was built with radial symmetry (which means the lines radiate out from one center point) and concentric circles and squares (one inside the other, sharing the same center point).

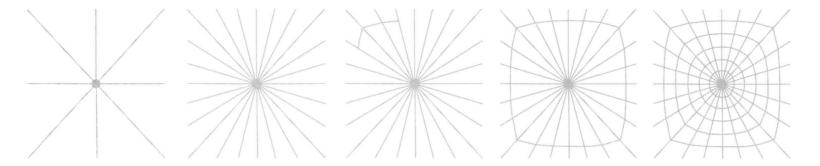

Trace, then write.

Length

Length

Length measure the distance between

two points. It can also mean the

longest dimension of an object.

Trace, then write.

Line

line

A line is a one-dimensional collection of

points extending in opposite directions.

Set of Two

These euphorbia flowers have only two petals. Can you think of other things that grow in sets of two?

Mm

Trace, then write.

Meter   meter

A meter is a unit for measuring

distance in the metric system. One

meter equals 100 centimeters.

Mmmmm

Mmm Mmm Mmm Mmm

Trace, then write.

metric — metric

The metric system is an international

system of measurement based on

multiples of ten.

Bilateral Symmetry

All animals show symmetry. This ladybug shows bilateral symmetry in its shape and the number of its spots; the right and left halves of its body are mirror images of each other.

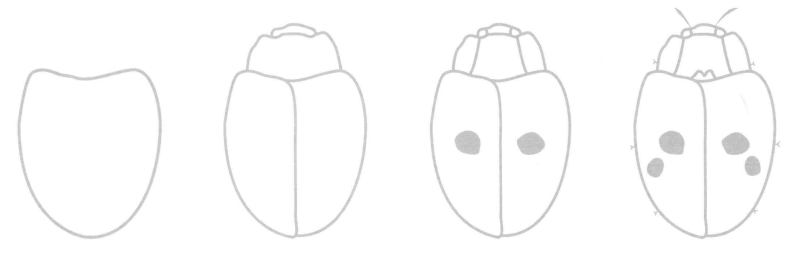

Trace, then write.

m m m m m m m m

m m m m m m m m m m m m

mile mile mile

A mile is a unit for measuring

distance. One mile equals 5,280 feet.

Mm

Trace, then write.

Minuend   minuend

In subtraction, the minuend is the

number from which another number is

taken away.

Symmetrical Spots

Ladybugs come in many different colors and have different numbers of spots.
This ladybug's sixteen spots are symmetrical—the same number and pattern on each side.

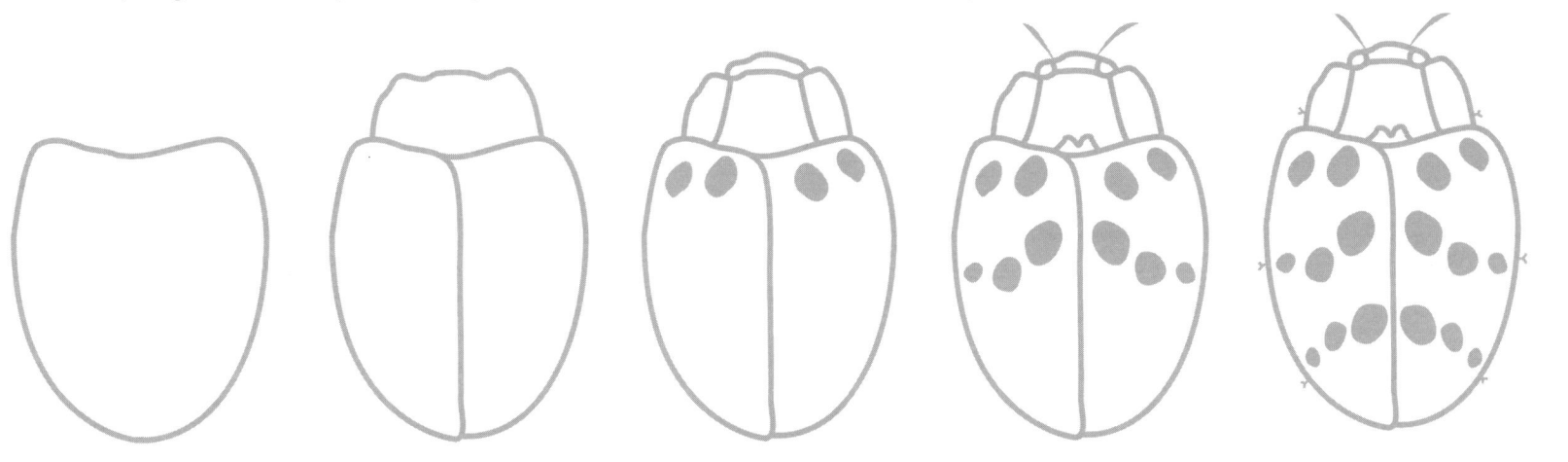

Mm

Trace, then write.

Multiplication

Multiplication is an operation that

adds a number a certain number of

times.

Trace, then write.

Num

Natural Numbers

Natural (counting) numbers are whole

numbers greater than zero.

Spiral

The nautilus shell grows in a spiral shape. Can you think of other spirals in nature?

Num

Trace, then write.

Negative Numbers

Negative numbers are numbers less

than zero.

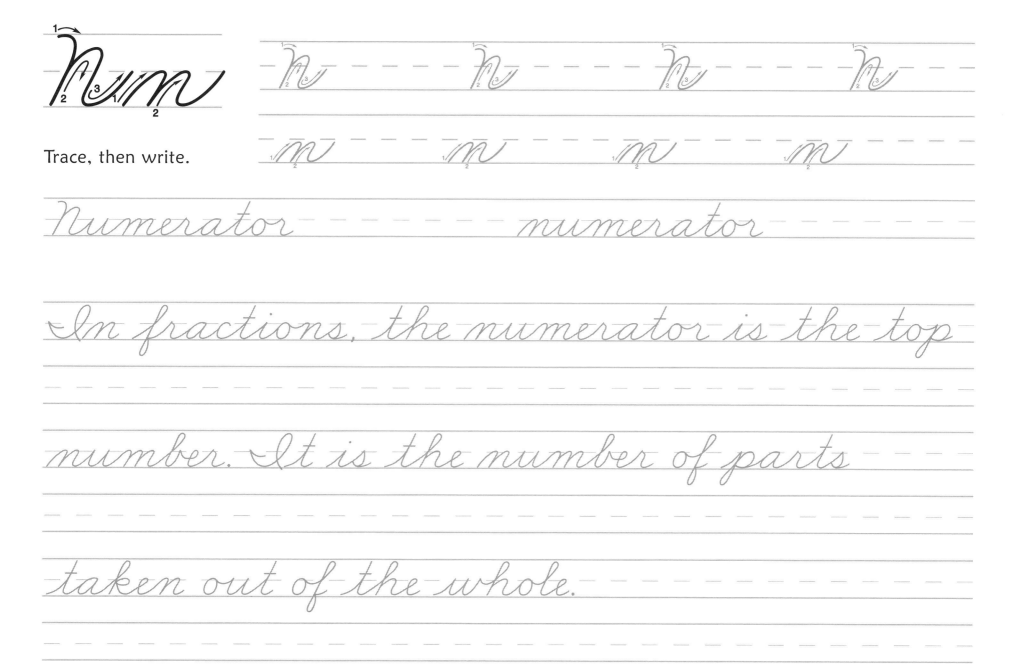

Trace, then write.

Numerator   numerator

In fractions, the numerator is the top

number. It is the number of parts

taken out of the whole.

Line of Symmetry

Moths and butterflies are symmetrical. Their body forms the line of symmetry down the center.

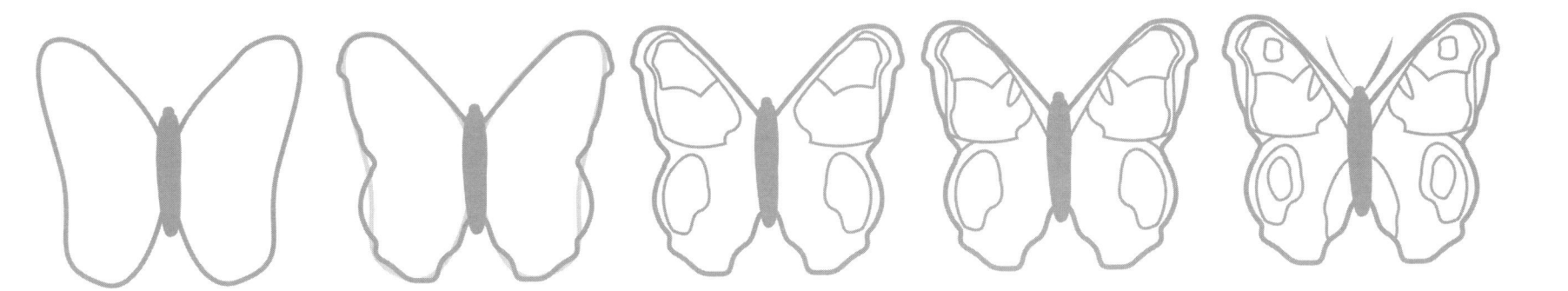

Trace, then write.

Obtuse   obtuse

An obtuse angle is an angle that

measures between 90 and 180 degrees.

Trace, then write.

Odd Numbers

An odd number is a number that

cannot be divided evenly by the

number 2.

Free Drawing

Trace, then write.

Operations

The four operations of arithmetic are

addition, subtraction, multiplication,

and division.

Parallel   parallel

Two lines are parallel if they stay the

same distance apart and do not

intersect.

Set of Six

Snowflakes are all unique, but they often form a six-sided shape.

Connect the tips of this snowflake and you will form a hexagon, which is a shape with six equal sides.

Trace, then write.

Parallelogram

A parallelogram is a quadrilateral

that has two pairs of parallel sides.

Trace, then write.

Percent   *percent*   *Percent*

A percent is a certain number of parts

per 100. It is shown using the % sign.

Parallel Lines

This copperband butterfly fish has parallel lines on its body.
Parallel lines are straight lines that are side by side but never touch.

Trace, then write.

Perimeter

The perimeter is the distance around

the edge of a closed, two-dimensional

shape.

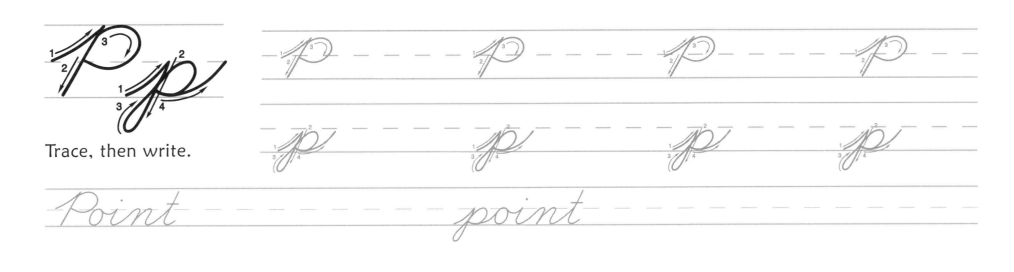

Trace, then write.

Point   point

A point is an exact position on a line,

on a flat surface, or in space.

Fibonacci Numbers

Many things grow in sets of the Fibonacci numbers. This Shasta daisy grew twenty-one petals. To find the Fibonacci numbers, start with 0 and 1. Add them together to get the next number, which would be one. Keep adding the last two numbers together to get the next number in the sequence. (0, 1, 1, 2, 3, 5, 8, 13, 21, and so on.)

Trace, then write.

Polygon   polygon

A polygon is a two-dimensional shape

made of three or more connected line

segments.

Trace, then write.

P p

Product   product

In multiplication, the product is the

result of repeatedly adding a number a

certain number of times.

Golden Rectangle

A golden rectangle is a special rectangle that occurs often in nature. To draw a golden rectangle, first draw a square. Next, draw a line from the center of one of the sides to an opposite corner. Imagine the line is attached to the square at the middle point and swing it up like the hands of a clock. This forms the long side of the golden rectangle. The short side of the golden rectangle is the length of the square you began with.

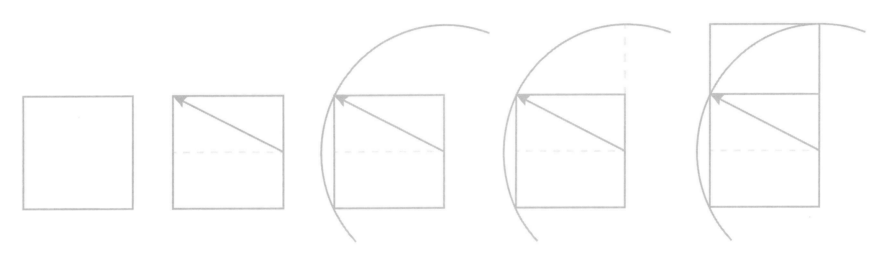

Trace, then write.

P   P   P   P

P   P   P   P

Pyramid   pyramid

A pyramid is a solid shape with five

faces. It has a square on the bottom

and four triangles on the sides.

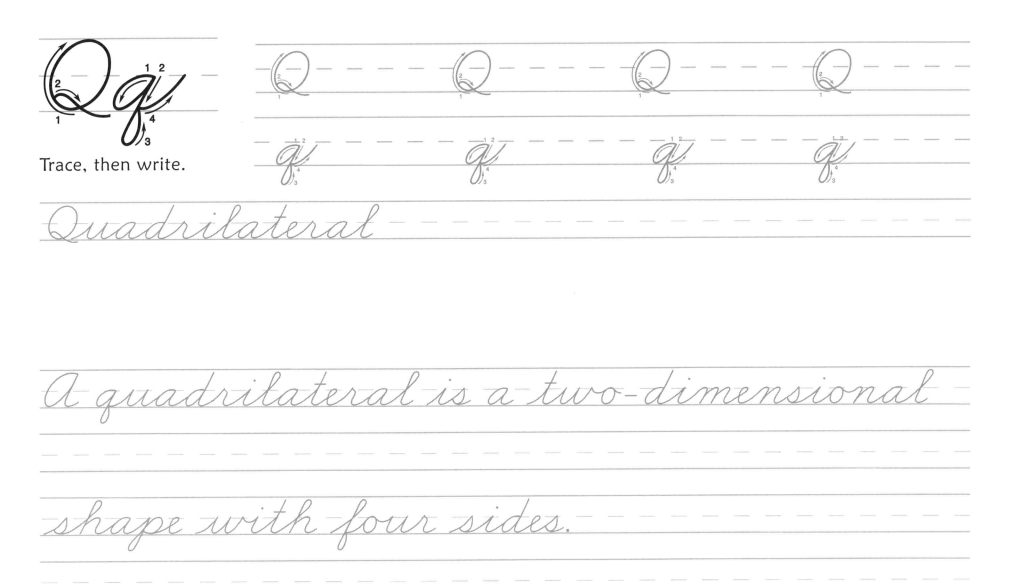

Trace, then write.

Quadrilateral

A quadrilateral is a two-dimensional

shape with four sides.

Symmetrical Pattern

Butterflies, like moths, have symmetrical body shapes and symmetrical patterns on their wings.

Q q

Trace, then write.

Q   Q   Q   Q

q   q   q   q

Quotient   quotient

In division, the quotient is the result

of splitting one number into a certain

number of equal parts.

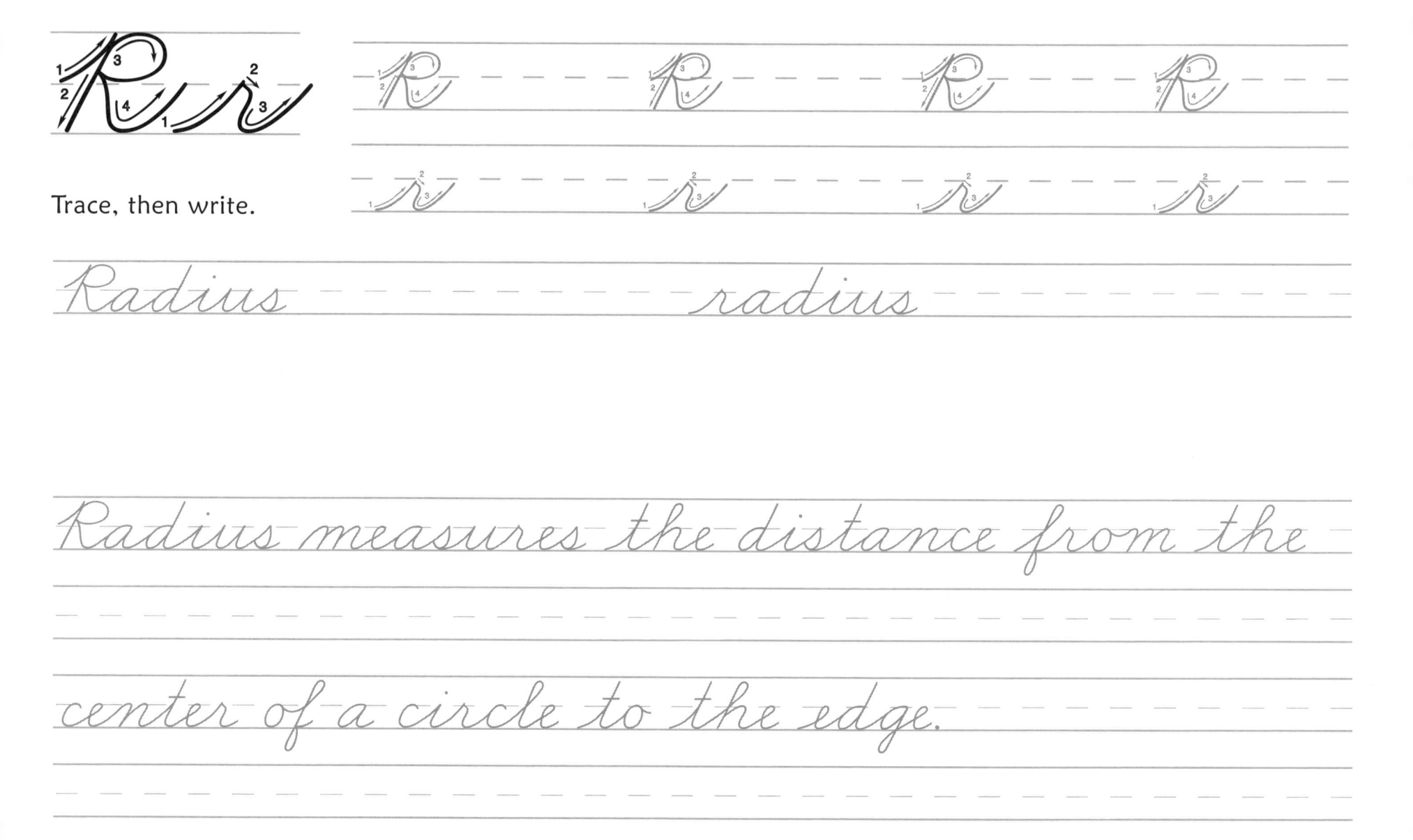

Trace, then write.

Radius   radius

Radius measures the distance from the

center of a circle to the edge.

Sphere

The earth is a sphere, which means it is the shape of a ball. Draw horizontal (lying down) parallel lines across a circle, then draw curved vertical (standing up) lines as shown to create a drawing that looks like a sphere.

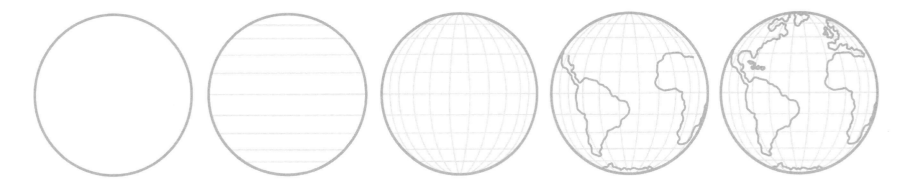

R r

Trace, then write.

Rectangle   rectangle

A rectangle is a quadrilateral with

four right angles.

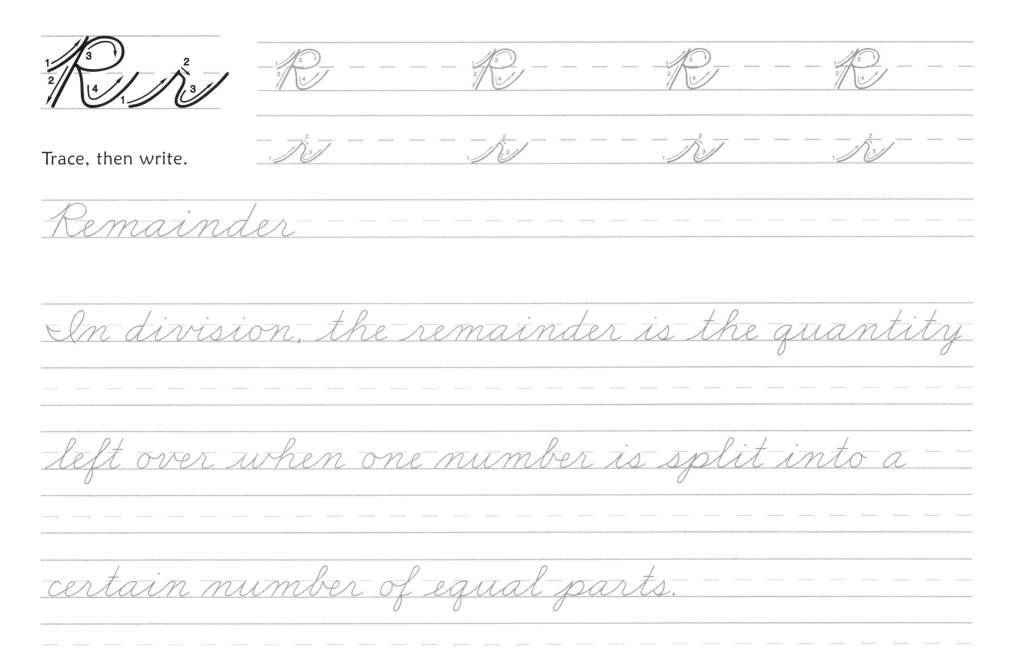

Trace, then write.

Remainder

In division, the remainder is the quantity

left over when one number is split into a

certain number of equal parts.

Spiral

Sunflower seeds grow in spirals, spinning out from the center.

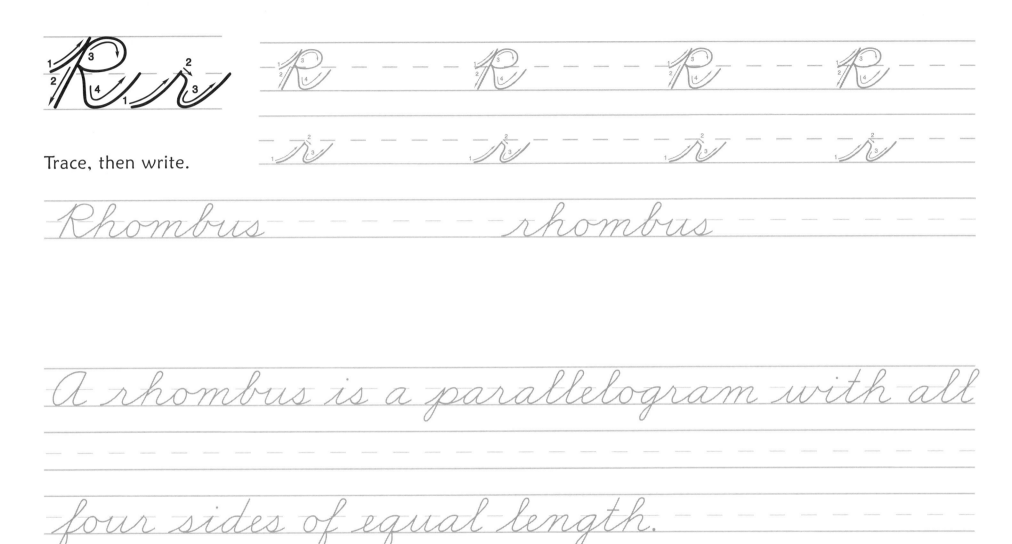

Trace, then write.

Rhombus   rhombus

A rhombus is a parallelogram with all

four sides of equal length.

R r

Trace, then write.

R R R R

r r r r

Right Angle

A right angle is an angle measuring

exactly 90 degrees, or one-fourth of a circle.

Pattern

The eastern diamondback rattlesnake is poisonous, but it has a beautiful pattern on its back. The diamond shape is repeated down its back.

Trace, then write.

R R R R

r r r r

Right Triangle

A right triangle is a triangle in which

one of the angles is a right angle.

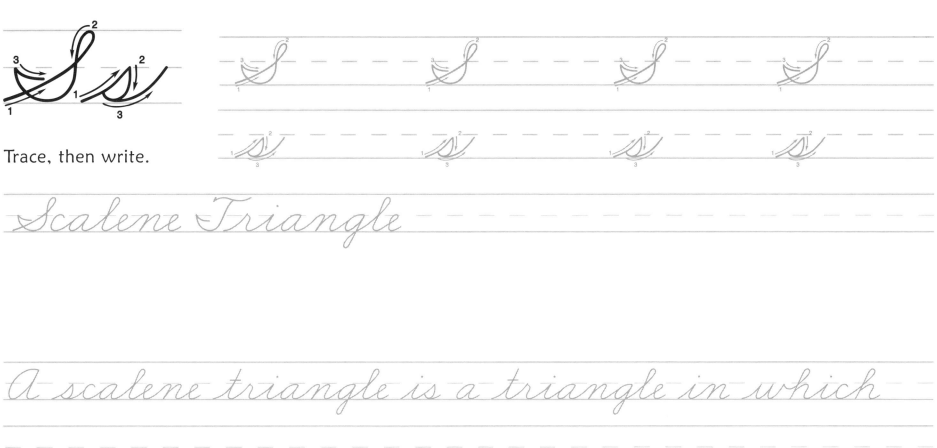

Trace, then write.

Scalene Triangle

A scalene triangle is a triangle in which

none of the sides are the same length.

Free Drawing

Trace, then write.

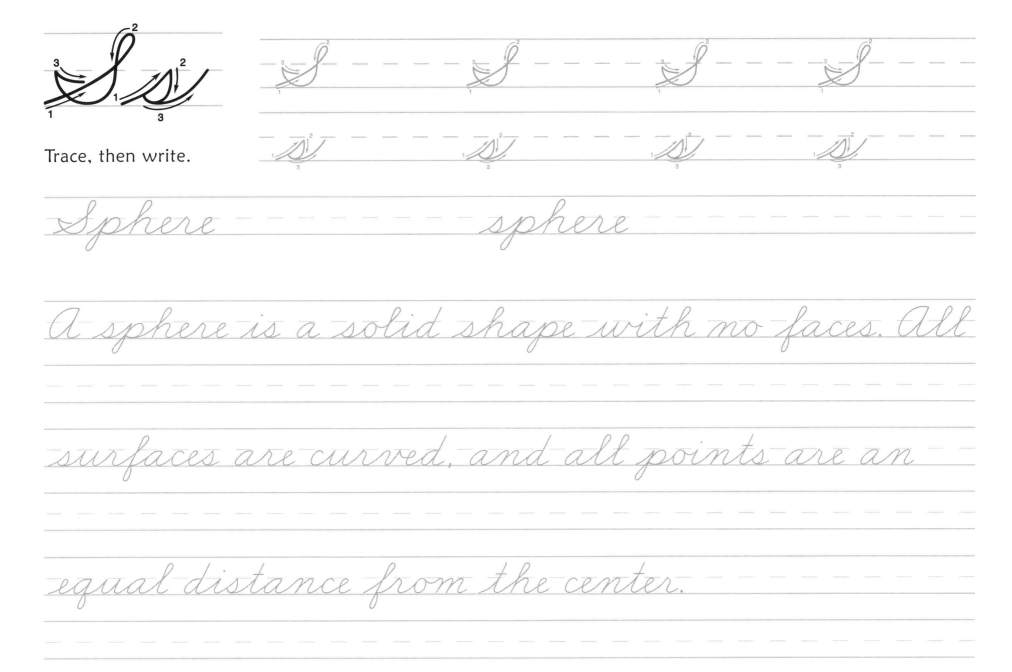

Sphere   sphere

A sphere is a solid shape with no faces. All

surfaces are curved, and all points are an

equal distance from the center.

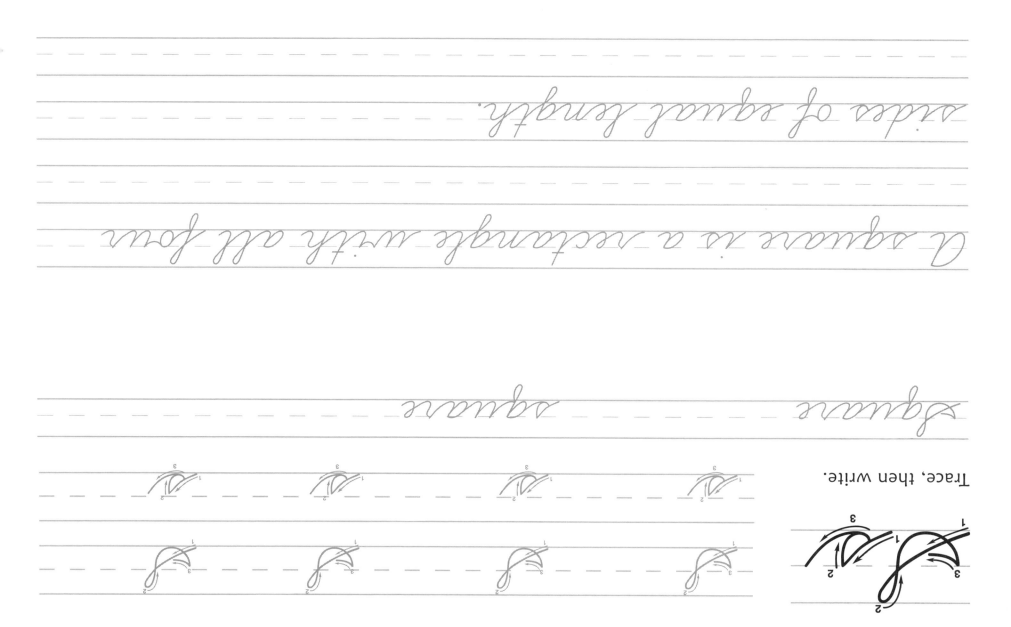

Trace, then write.

square   square

A square is a rectangle with all four
sides of equal length.

Fibonacci Numbers

Many plants grow branches following the Fibonacci numbers. Trace this one and notice that it starts with zero branches, and grows one branch. That one branch grows into two branches, then to three, and so on in the Fibonacci sequence (5, 8, and 13).

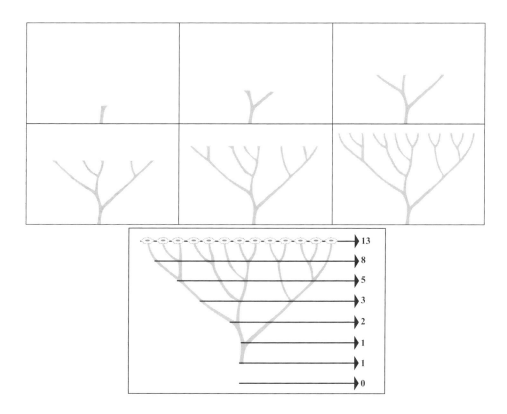

Trace, then write.

Square Unit

A square unit is one unit wide and one unit high. It is used to measure area.

Trace, then write.

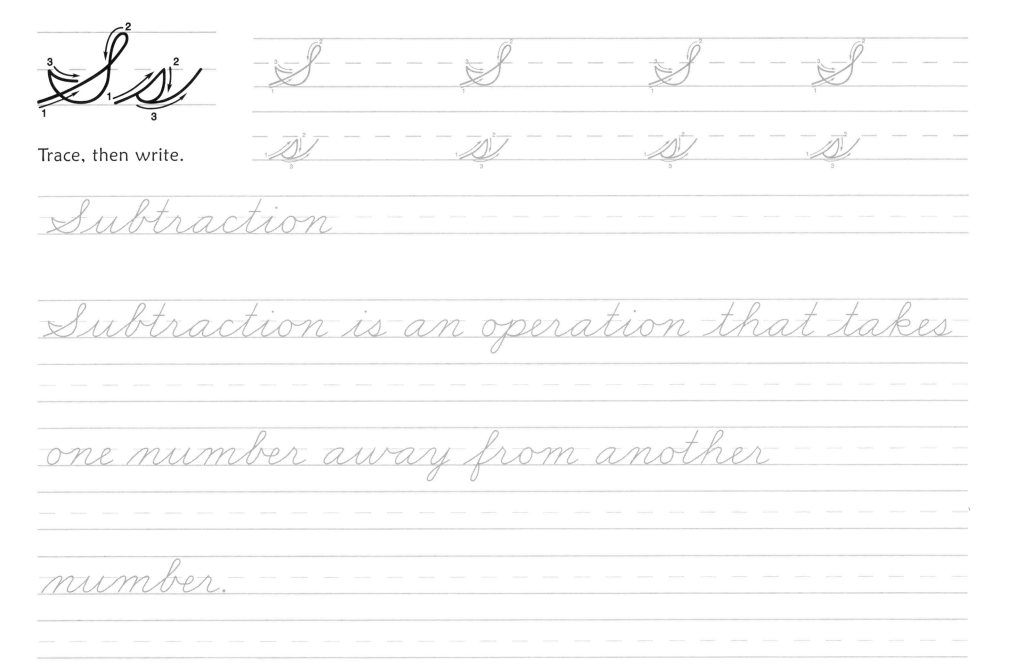

Subtraction

Subtraction is an operation that takes

one number away from another

number.

Symmetry

Maybe the reason that we find symmetry attractive is because we are symmetrical ourselves.
Use a light center line to help you draw human faces that are symmetrical.

Trace, then write.

Subtrahend

In subtraction, the subtrahend is the

number that is taken away from

another number.

bringing together two or more numbers.

In addition, the sum is the result of

Sum Sum

Trace, then write.

Parallel Lines

On this eastern black swallowtail caterpillar, you can see parallel lines across its body.

Trace, then write.

Triangle   triangle

A triangle is a two-dimensional shape

with three straight sides and three

corners.

Trace, then write.

U.S. Customary System

The U.S. customary system is a system

of measurement using pounds, gallons,

and feet.

Parallel Lines

This male ladybird spider has white parallel lines on all eight of his black legs. With his black head and bright red body, he is quite a showy fellow! Notice the arrangement of four black dots in a square shape on his back as well.

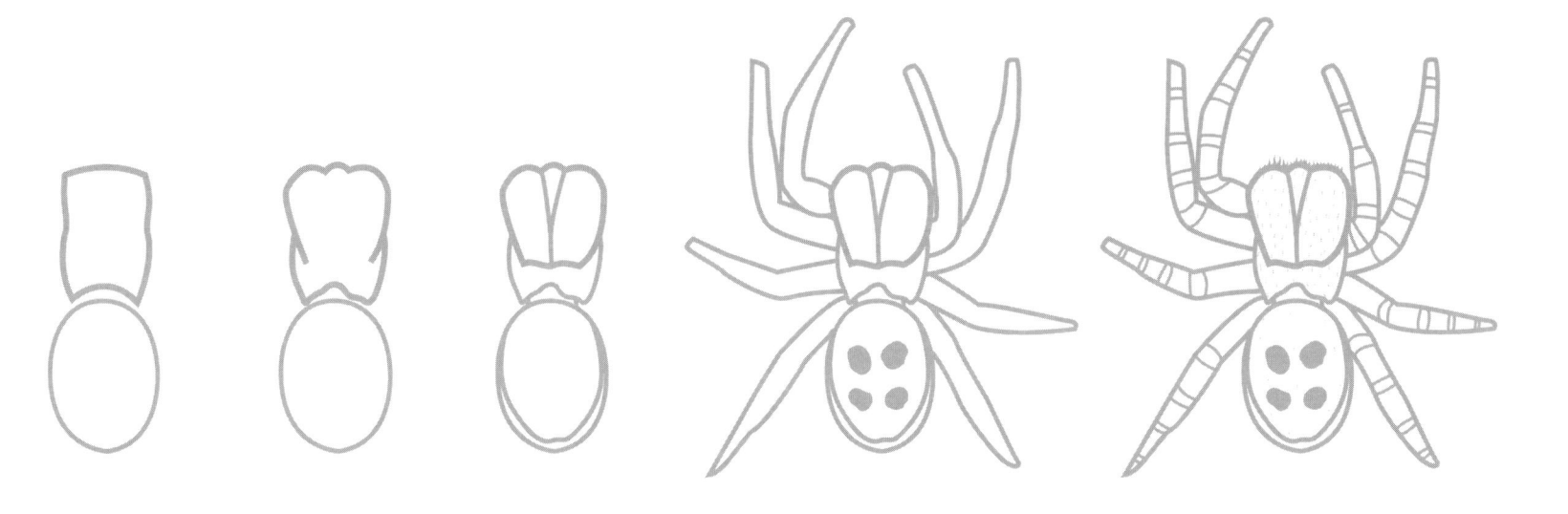

Trace, then write.

Variable   variable

A variable is a letter used to represent

an unknown number.

Trace, then write.

Vv

Volume   *Volume*

Volume means the amount of space a

solid shape occupies. Volume is measured

in cubic units.

Spiral

Chameleons are unique lizards. They curl their tail into a spiral shape when they are not using it to hold onto a tree branch. They can change colors, too, according to their mood or the light. You might see chameleons that are green, yellow, orange, red, pink, or blue.

Ounces and grams are units of weight.

Weight measures how heavy an object is.

Weight weight Weight

Trace, then write.

Ww Ww

Trace, then write.

Whole Numbers

Trace.

A whole number refers to a set of
numbers (0, 1, 2, 3...) that can be
written without a fraction or decimal
and are greater than or equal to zero.

Parallel Lines and Dots

Poison dart frogs have many colors and patterns.

This one has parallel lines down his back and spots on his legs.

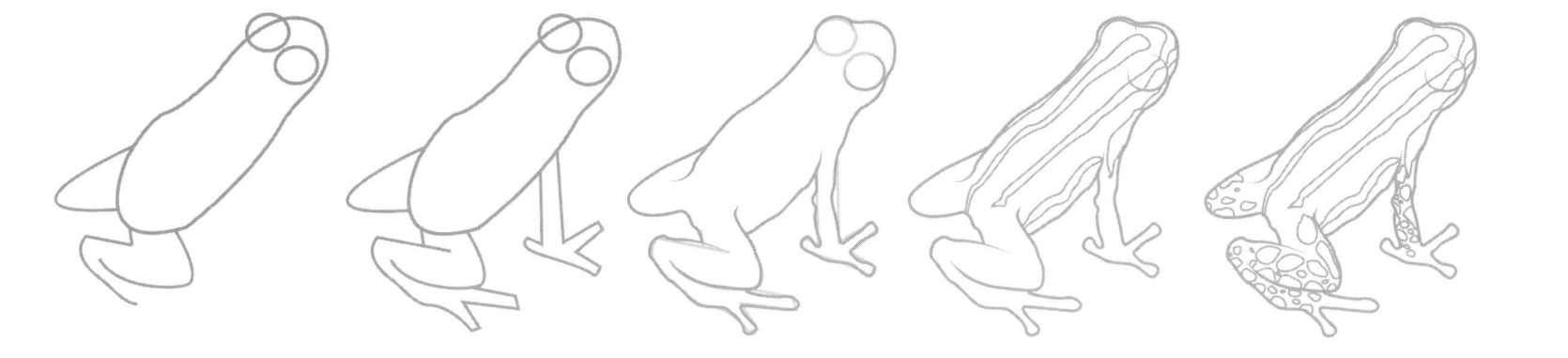

Trace, then write.

Width   width

Width measures the horizontal distance

from one side of an object to the other

side.

Trace, then write.

𝒳𝓊

𝒳 𝒳 𝒳 𝒳

𝓍 𝓍 𝓍 𝓍

X-axis X-axis X-axis

The x-axis is the horizontal axis on a
plane coordinate system.

Symmetry and Concentric Circles

A peacock spreads his beautiful tail to reveal a radial pattern of lines and spots of concentric circles.
The circles look like eyes, which helps scare away predators.

One yard equals three feet.

A yard is a unit of measuring distance.

yard ----- yard ----- yard

y y y y

h h h h

Trace, then write.

y

Trace, then write.

Y Y Y Y

y y y y

Y-axis   y-axis

The y-axis is the vertical axis on a

plane coordinate system.

Parallel Lines

Zebras have a pattern of alternating black and white stripes. Try coloring every other stripe black on this zebra. Keep the stripes symmetrical (the same on both sides).

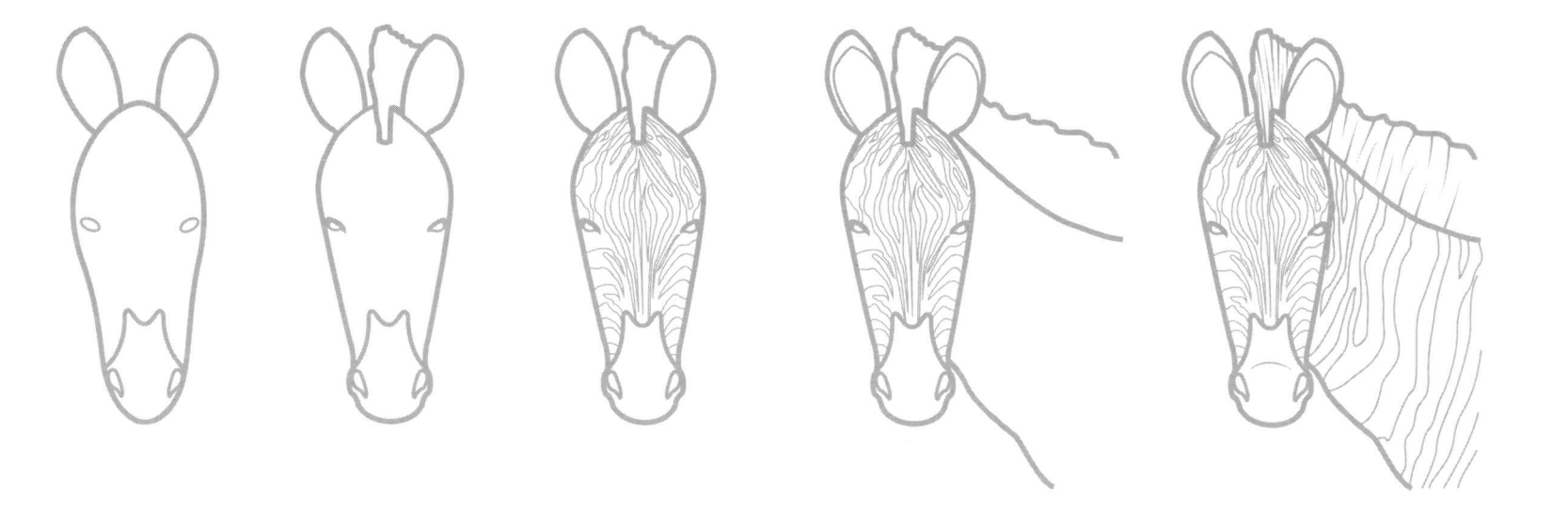

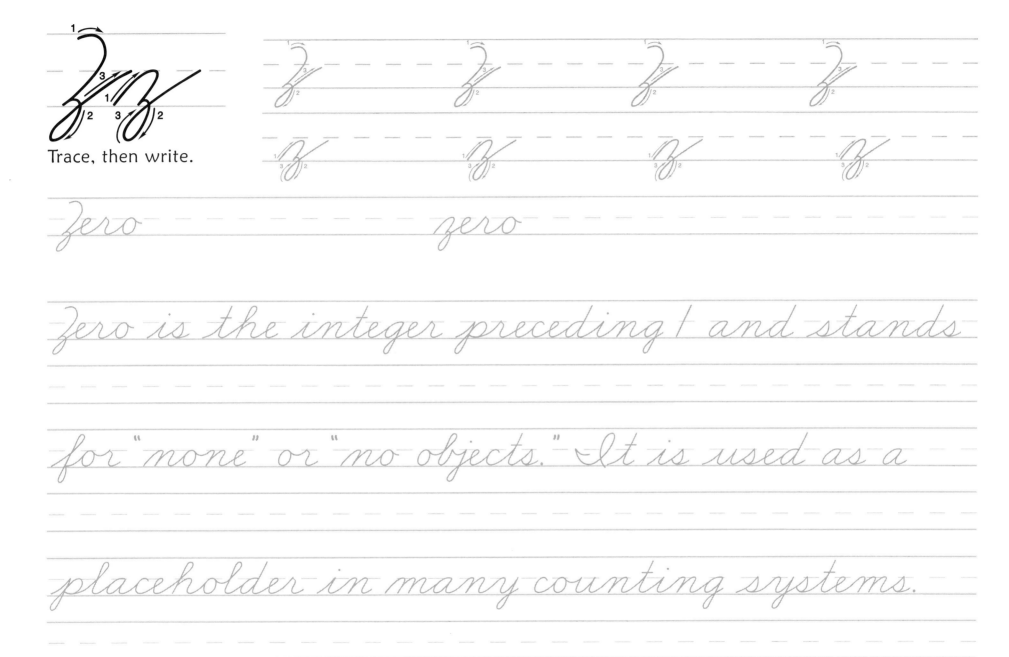

Trace, then write.

zero zero

Zero is the integer preceding 1 and stands

for "none" or "no objects." It is used as a

placeholder in many counting systems.

Free Drawing

Index of Math Terms Used in Cursive Copywork

Acute 11
Addend................................ 12
Addition 14
Angle................................... 15
Area..................................... 17
Associative Law........... 18, 20
Bisect 21
Centimeter....................... 23
Circle.................................. 24
Circumference 26
Commutative Law....... 27, 29
Cone 30
Cube................................... 32
Cylinder 33
Decimal Numbers 35
Degree................................ 36
Denominator..................... 38
Diameter............................ 39
Difference 41
Distributive Law 42
Dividend 44
Division............................. 45
Divisor 47
Equation 48
Equilateral........................ 50
Even Numbers.................. 51
Factor................................. 53
Fibonacci Numbers 54
Foot 56

Fraction 57
Geometry 59
Height 60
Identity Law 62, 63
Inch 65
Integer 66
Intersect............................ 68
Isosceles 69
Joule.................................. 71
Kilometer.......................... 72
Length............................... 74
Line 75
Meter................................. 77
Metric................................ 78
Mile 80
Minuend............................ 81
Multiplication................... 83
Natural Numbers.............. 84
Negative Numbers 86
Numerator 87
Obtuse............................... 89
Odd Numbers 90
Operations 92
Parallel.............................. 93
Parallelogram.................... 95
Percent.............................. 96
Perimeter 98
Point.................................. 99
Polygon 101

Product 102
Pyramid 104
Quadrilateral................... 105
Quotient........................... 107
Radius.............................. 108
Rectangle 110
Remainder 111
Rhombus.......................... 113
Right Angle...................... 114
Right Triangle 116
Scalene Triangle.............. 117
Sphere.............................. 119
Square.............................. 120
Square Unit 122
Subtraction...................... 123
Subtrahend...................... 125
Sum.................................. 126
Triangle 128
U.S. Customary System.. 129
Variable 131
Volume............................. 132
Weight.............................. 134
Whole Numbers.............. 135
Width 137
X-axis 138
Yard 140
Y-axis 141
Zero 143

Index of Terms Used in Drawing Lessons

Sphere (Whole Orange)..............................13

Five-pointed Star (Tomato) 16

Cone (Volcano)..19

Concentric Circles (Tree Stump)...............22

Alternating Patterns (Leaf Veins) 25

Five-pointed Star (Apple Seeds)................28

Five-pointed Star (Star Fruit)....................31

Set of Three (Clover) 34

Radial Symmetry (Orange Slice)...............40

Five-pointed Star (Brittle Starfish)...........43

Hexagon (Beehive) 46

Set of Four (Four-leaf Clover) 49

Symmetry (Leaves on a Branch)................52

One (Calla Lily)..55

Set of Three (Tomato Slice) 58

Set of Three (Trillium Flower) 61

Set of Five (Columbine Flower)..................67

Set of Four (Dogwood Flower) 70

Radial Symmetry (Spider Web).................73

Set of Two (Euphorbia Flowers)................76

Bilateral Symmetry (Ladybug) 79

Symmetrical Spots (Ladybug) 82

Spiral (Nautilus Shell)................................85

Line of Symmetry (Moth) 88

Set of Six (Snowflake) 94

Parallel Lines (Copperband Butterfly
   Fish) 97

Fibonacci Numbers (Shasta Daisy)..........100

Golden Rectangle 103

Symmetrical Pattern (Butterfly)..............106

Sphere (Earth)..109

Spiral (Sunflower Seeds) 112

Pattern (Eastern Diamondback
   Rattlesnake) 115

Fibonacci Numbers (Plant Branch)..........121

Symmetry (Human Face) 124

Parallel Lines (Eastern Black
   Swallowtail Caterpillar) 127

Parallel Lines (Ladybird Spider)..............130

Spiral (Chameleon) 133

Parallel Lines and Dots
   (Poison Dart Frog)................................136

Symmetry and Concentric
   Circles (Peacock) 139

Parallel Lines (Zebra) 142